More Grandma Jan's Poems

For Kids and Grandkids and Pet Lovers Too

Jan Unger

To Laila ~
For you & me,
It's poetry.
Enjoy!

(aunt) Jan Unger

Private Label Publishing
Colorado Springs CO

First Printing December 2012
©2012 Jan Unger

Published by
Private Label Publishing
6180 Lehman Drive Suite 104
Colorado Springs, CO 80918
719-266-0437 / 800-266-0999
www.privatelabelpublishing.com
info@privatelabelpublishing.com

Made in the United States of America

ISBN 978-1-61888-040-6

On Grandma Jan's front door there's a sign
That welcomes each and every canine.

They come in every color and size,
Each one could win a "Westminster" prize.

When people ask me, I must admit,
The one I have with me is my favorite.

I love them all (I'm a grandmother, you know),
I wish I could keep them, but home they must go.

My Friend Pepper

Pepper's my favorite 100-lb. Lab,
It's mostly muscle, and a little flab.

When I'm home she's as good as can be,
But when I'm not, she really misses me.

One day I came home, found wrappers on the
floor,
With her paw, she had opened a drawer.

My cookies were missing,
Where could they be?
Pepper was hiding them
In her belly!!

My Friend Maggie

It's hard to write a poem about Maggie,
A "golden" whose coat's a little shaggy.
She's obedient and sweet,
Dog-sitting's a treat.
Her poop needs a very large baggie.

She loves to stare out the window,
And growl in a tone very low.
There's no one there,
A squirrel or a hare?
I guarantee there's a no-show.

Maggie loves to take a long walk,
No need to give a pep talk.
She's right at my side,
Stays right in stride,
At passing dogs she'll just gawk.

All dogs should be trained this well,
She'll bark when she hears the doorbell.
Maggie sleeps by my bed,
And loves to be fed,
I will hate to bid "fare-thee-well."

My Friend Ellie

Ellie's an Australian shepherd with lots of fur,
She loves it when I comb and brush her.

She's mostly black with white paws and chest,
She could almost win a beauty contest.

When walking she's as good as can be,
Except when chasing a squirrel up a tree.

Ellie and I like to have lots of fun,
She would wag her tail, but she doesn't have one.

My Friend Lucy

Lucy is high energy and lots of fun,
To the end of the leash she likes to run.

Winter, spring, summer, fall,
Which are her favorite ones of all?

Winter, when there's snow all around,
She eats the powder right off the ground.

But her favorite season is really autumn,
When the color of trees is truly awesome.

If the wind is blowing, hold on to Lucy -- Good Grief!
Her mission in life is to catch EVERY LEAF!

My Friend Mattie

Mattie's a blue-heeler with spotted fur,
She loves a belly rub, that's for sure.

When Mattie eats, she wants company,
I'll sit alongside 'til her bowl is empty.

She doesn't bark or let out a wail,
Someone gave her a very strange tail.

Mattie's so good, she's a sweetie pie,
But who punched her and gave her a black eye?

My Friend Popeye

Popeye's a Maltese terrier, who could be a movie star,
When walking, he puts on the brakes, won't go very far.

He doesn't eat spinach, and flips up his kibble,
When in the right mood, he'll just take a nibble.

His two black button-eyes stare up at you,
If there's a cuter 7~pounder, I'd like to know who.

Popeye loves it when he's in his coop,
But the best part of all is his little poop

My Friend Abby

Abby's a dachshund with a tail like a fan.
She loves it when there's food in her pan.

I took her to visit the people next door,
She hopped into the kitchen to clean up their floor.

Each morning she'll lick me for about an hour,
I'm saving water, no need for a shower.

Abby's ears are long and fly out,
Her tail dusts the ground when we're out and about.

She is a love, so sweet and so good,
If you don't want to keep her, I'll take her, I would.

My Friends Stuart and Charles

Have you ever heard of an Egyptian Mau?
It's a breed of cats my neighbor has now.

Stuart and Charles come from the very same litter,
They both visit their boxes of kitty-litter.

Their bodies are grey, but one has white feet,
They slink around and are very sweet.

I care for them whenever I'm able,
They're sometimes hiding or up on a table.

Give them food, water -- so easy to care for,
Visit once a day, and I'm out the door.

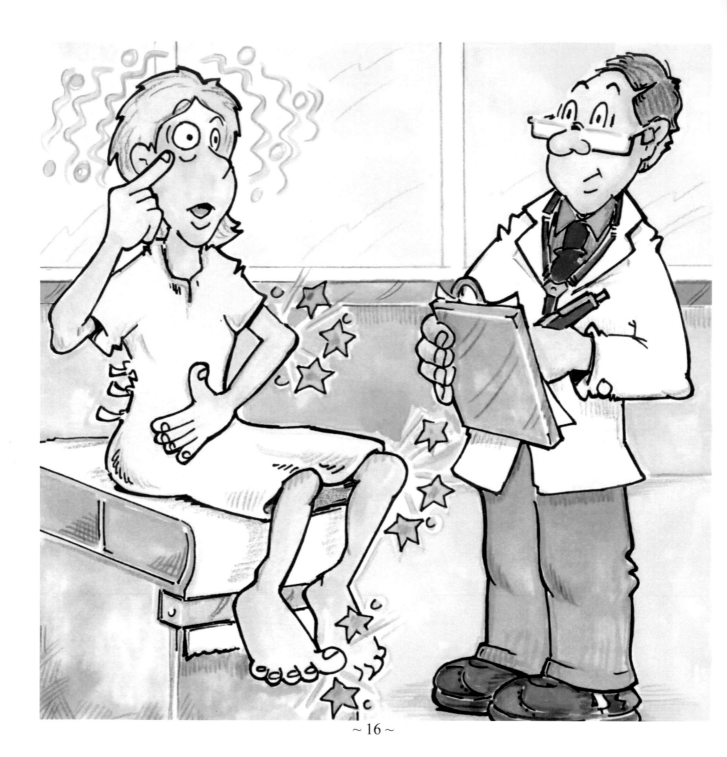

A Visit to the Doctor

Doctor, doctor, can you see
What is terribly wrong with me?

It hurts to bend my left elbow,
I have a pain in my big toe.

My belly aches after pizza pie,
And I'm seeing double from my right eye.

My head spins when I get up fast,
I don't know if I'm going to last.

The worst of all is my aching "flea-bitis,"
The doctor says,
"You've got hypochondriac-itis!"

House for Sale

Leaving the east for the "Western Trail,"
We put our house on the market "for sale."

The real estate salesman did require
We vacate our home for a potential buyer.

My husband and I went on a vacation,
And returned to our home with great expectation.

A strange car was parked in front of our home,
Was our house being shown while we did roam?

We parked down the street, waited two hours or so,
Nobody came out, so home we did go.

The realtor was nowhere in sight,
My neighbor had parked his car overnight.

A Trip to Your Dentist

Visiting your dentist can be lots of fun,
If cavities . . . you have none.

Hop in the chair, open your mouth wide,
The dentist would like to look inside.

Brush your teeth morning and night,
So your teeth will shine, nice and white.

See your dentist twice a year,
You then can smile from ear to ear.

Take care of your teeth, as you are told,
Hopefully you'll still have them when you're old.

What's In a Name?

People's names can be very funny,
The weather is either a "Storm" or it's "Sonny."

Months are "April," "May," or "June."
Flowers are "Lily," "Iris," "Rose," or "Petune(ia)."

A bird could be a "Robin" or a "Jay,"
"Tuesday" is the name of a day.

Brown "Betty" is a dessert good to eat,
And "Candy" can be terribly sweet.

We say "Grace" before we eat "Stu,"
Is "Violet" a shade of blue?

People's names can be very funny.
A "Bea" is buzzing around you, "Honey."

My Post Office

It's no wonder the post office has financial woes,
And some of its mail centers are about to close.

Weeks before Christmas there's just one clerk on the floor,
While customers are lined up out the front door.

People want to send their packages off quick,
In hopes of arriving in time for St. Nick.

I have found the ideal time to go,
Is the day after Christmas when it is slow.

My Hole in One?

Golf is a passion for many folks,
The object: to have the fewest strokes.

I was playing a local course one day,
A par-three hole wasn't far away.

It was winter and on the green
Was a diffcrent hole which couldn't be seen.

I struck my ball, and it disappeared,
We wouldn't find it, oh, how I feared.

Lo and behold, it was in the cup,
But not the one with the flag sticking up.

Water Aerobics

Water aerobics at the "Ys,"
A wonderful way to exercise.

Moving your muscles in the warm water,
Keeps your body in good working order.

Meet new friends and chat awhile,
Each teacher has her very own style.

So, if your joints ache and you're eighty-two,
Come to the pool, your body will thank you.

The Elderly Sisters' Reunion

I have two sisters, and I love them dearly,
We meet each other in Boston, yearly.

We travel from three distant locations
To meet each other on vacations.

We are seniors in our eighties,
Lost our hubbies, now single ladies.

Each of us wears a hearing-aid item,
We inherited from parents a hearing problem.

When we get together, we talk a lot,
But most of the time, it's "WHAT?" "WHAT?" "WHAT?"

Our Trip to the Panama Canal

If you are looking for a great vacation,
Take a cruise to a foreign destination.
My sister and I wanted to celebrate
90 and 80 years since our birth date.

We boarded "The Princess," went to our room,
Waiting for us were two bouquets in full bloom.
There were platters of food, and lots of gifts,
Sent by all our thoughtful relatives.

We traveled south in the Caribbean,
Visiting ports neither one of us had seen.
French builders of the "canal" were struck with small pox,
So Americans took over and built the Panama locks.

Guided by rail cars our ship glided on,
After rising three chambers we were in Lake Gatun.
Our ship turned around, through the locks to the "Sea,"
Costa Rica was our next destiny.

A rain forest, gondola ride, and waterfall,
We hiked, got wet, and had a ball.
The Island Princess is a floating city,
Restaurants, pools, a spa ~~ every amenity.

Watch a show, a movie, eat a pizza, or ice cream cone,
Dance, gamble, walk the deck, or just be alone.
Go on a cruise, be pampered, and relax,
Forget your troubles, and your income tax.

A Trip to the Bowling Alley

Bowling is a wonderful sport,
All people can do it, tall or short.

Young or old, or in between,
Scoring is done by the alley's machine.

It's not as easy as it looks,
The ball rolls right or sometimes hooks.

The object is to hit the most pins that you can,
A strike or a spare should be your game plan.

You can bowl for fun or compete in a league,
It's not too strenuous nor causes fatigue.

A kid's birthday party can be a real treat,
With bowling and cake for all to eat.

So, take a friend or your family,
Go have some fun at your bowling alley.

My Golf Game

My golf lately has been a disaster,
Because this game is difficult to master.

Every muscle goes a different way,
I try my best to turn, not to sway.

I must remember, "It's only a game,"
And I'll never make the "Golf Hall of Fame."

So, because my ball doesn't go very far,
I'm changing my name to "Anita Par."

Writing a Book

Writing a book I thought was a snap,
Until I found it was much more than that.

Finding a publisher, you could go berserk,
Choosing one who approves of your work.

Your book must be edited and then proof-read,
It must be perfect before it is print-ed.

Your "baby" might become an "American Idol,"
So give it a name with a proper title.

The publishing process could drive you insane,
Like having a baby, it's a real "labor pain."

Unless you are one who has plenty of clout,
It's pacing and waiting for "it" to "come out!"

Electronic Toys

What will the electronic inventors think up next?
Will it be one on which we can still text?

Spelling correctly has become obsolete,
Now that we twitter and sometimes tweet.

Alexander Bell's phone is a thing of the past,
A mobile unit is how we broadcast.

So stop living in cyberspace,
Discard your toys and speak face to face.

A Trip to the Zoo

Have a day with nothing to do?
Plan a trip to visit the zoo.

Old or young must pay a fee,
What kind of animals will we see?

Lions, tigers, and even giraffes,
Swinging monkeys will give us laughs.

Budgies in an aviary can be fed,
Oops, did something wet just hit my head?

Baby gorillas nurse at a breast,
When nature's wildlife is at its best.

See it all at the city zoo,
You may ask yourself, "What's (a) gnu?"

Bullying

What is a bully? Can you please tell me?
It's a person who is a real "meanie."

A bully picks on one who is weak or small,
No reason to do that, it's not nice at all.

If a bully would walk in the other's shoes,
That bad behavior he would not choose.

Be considerate and kind and you will see,
That no one likes a big bully.

Respect

Are your folks always telling you
What to do and what not to do?

Are you listening and do you obey?
Always wanting to get your own way?

Honor your elders and follow their lead,
They have lived longer and can help you succeed.

Honesty

You know you should not tell a lie,
It leads to trouble, bye and bye.

Confess to what you have done wrong,
Tell the truth all along.

Please be honest, yes, you must.
It will build a lasting trust.

The Olympics

Watching the Olympics on T.V.
Is the greatest show that's for free.

The elite athletes all compete,
Keeping us all glued to our seat.

For some, the judges have to choose,
Who will win and who will lose.

For others, the "gold" is by score or speed,
It's a supreme effort which takes the lead.

Whether a medal or not, we agree,
We all are so proud of our country!

A Big Wide Smile

Life can be so much fun,
When you play outdoors in the sun.

Put a smile upon your face,
For the whole human race.

If your mouth has got a frown,
Turn that frown upside down.

Show how happy you can be,
For your friends and your family.